Penny's poetry

Penny Ashton

BookLeaf Publishing

India | USA | UK

Presentation by *BookLeaf Publishing*

Web: www.bookleafpub.com

E-mail: info@bookleafpub.com

ISBN: 9789358317404

First edition 2023

I dedicate this book to my dad.

ACKNOWLEDGEMENT

I'd like to thank my grandad who loves hearing my poems and encourages me to write more. i would also like to thank my mum for buying me my first ever book to write my poems in.

PREFACE

Although I am very young, I have been writing
poetry for a long time. This is my first
opportunity to share my work with the world.
When I wrote my first poem it inspired me to
write more. I love seeing the reaction of my
family and friends when I read them my poems.

Least, Not Most

I see the sunlight instead of the rain
Where I feel happiness, I used to feel pain.
Think about your future, instead of your past
Think about winning a race, but not about
coming last.
You want to feel at home
You dont want to feel lost.
Think about the people who have least, not
most.

One Stormy Night

One stormy night there's thunder and lightning
One stormy night there's something scary and
frightening
I hear noises, crashes and crying
As the wind howls it's almost like it growls
One stormy night it's all slippery and wet
Cold and rainy, I feel like it's very draining.
One stormy night it's scary all around
Tree's falling onto the ground.
One stormy night not a person in sight

It's Not You, It's Me

When you look down from the sky
You say it's not you, it's me
Am I lost in a dream or can I just not be seen
I see them glowing in the night
While I'm not burning so bright
Sail away in the black sea
And you say it's not you, it's me
I miss my past then I say that past, that past was
your last
One night you're the only person in the street
And you say It's not you, it's me.

Summer's Day

It's a summer's day and everyone is outside
Playing and splashing in the pool while some
people are on a roller coaster ride
I'm so hot and sweaty I can barely breathe
I think I might treat myself to an icecream
As the day goes by I notice something in the sky
The sun is gone and mist starts to come in
It starts to get cold while I start to get confused
about what's going on
Now it's a winter's day and everyone is inside
Watching and sleeping in front of the TV as the
day goes by.

The Vampire

We were moving house
And driving to our new destination
I thought the house was haunted
But no one else seemed to think it
We walked in the dark hallway
Red eyes everywhere
In the kitchen claw marks on the walls
Upstairs I heard screams
I went up nothing was there
Except for blood on the floor
It's in my house I don't know where it is
I hear it scraping it's fingers on the walls
As I get more scared I heard it's crawls
As I look into the dark hallway red eyes glaring
towards me
As I go to sleep you won't believe what I see
A vampire creeping at me.

The Beach

I like the beach the sand the sea
Oh and especially the sea shells when they make
the sound of the sea
It just makes me so happy
I like the sea when the waves splash upon me
Sometimes the sand is hot or cold
Hard or soft, crunchy or crispy
Depending on what it is I like to wander on the
beach
It makes me so happy I sometime screech
So I like the beach the sand the sea
Especially when the waves splash upon me

Syrup

I like syrup it has that sweet taste
Especially on my pancakes when it drips off my
plate
It's so sticky and cold it drips off my tongue
Especially on my strawberries
It makes them extra sweet
I love it with my icecream
Wow it's such a treat
I like syrup it has that sweet taste
Especially on my pancakes when it drips off my
plate.

Crisps

Who doesn't like crisps
They're crunchy with so much flavour
Especially when they're baked
Honestly they're my saviour
I like them with my lunch or for a midday snack
I love the smell of crisps when you first open the
pack
I cant' describe them they're so crispy, crunchy
and delicious
I think they're just so tasty
So who dosn't like crisps? because if you don't
I'll be on your door step in just a minute.

The Halloween Party

It's Halloween and the guests are on their way
I'm gonna lay out some snacks and make room
for the kids to play
I look out the window oh my gosh the guests are
here
As I go to the door they look at me with fear
I think it was because of my costume
Because I was dressed as a dead deer
So all the guests started entering
they all went to the dining room
where my family was waiting

Hello

Hello, Hola, Bonjour, Buongiorno,
How are you today?
Oh my gosh, i'm so pumped for the day
Hello, Hola, Bonjour, Buongiorno,
Would you like a glass of water?
Honestly, do you need anything?
Hello, Hola, Bonjour, Buongiorno,
Oh my gosh, when will the day be over?
I'm so tired and cold, I just want to go to bed!

The Hockey Match

As the match starts, I go on to my A-game
I hear the whistle blow. Oh my gosh the match
has started
I'm over here! I'm over here! I shout
They pass to me as I start to freak out
I shoot down the pitch with the hockey ball on
my stick
Ok here I go I say. I shoot, I score!
Well that wasn't so bad, I say to myself
As my team mates come to high five me, I
realise we've won the hockey match.

Music

Music makes me dance
It makes me want to prance
My favourite music is pop, what's yours, rock?
When there is silence in my house
I drown it out by singing opera
I don't think anyone likes it too much
Music makes me dance
It makes me want to prance

Your Happy Place

I feel indescribable, untraceable
But when you are surrounded by the people that
you love, you've found your place
Your happy place
And nothing will change that feeling
Because, in the end, your family will be that one
happy place
To keep building you up, and up, until you fall
But when you fall, get back up again and carry
on.

The Talented Kangaroo

This kangaroo can leap, jump, sing, and dance
Everything but a prance
He can fly, jump, kick, sniff
He can even eat a walnut whip!
It looks like he can also flip
He can back flip, front flip
He can also land on his big cute fat flat face
There he goes, he knocked over a vase, in a very
small space!

The Zoo Animals

The snake slithers
the lion roars
the monkey laughs
the pig snorts
the elephant has some hungry thoughts
the rhino is about to break everything he sees if
he doesn't have his treats
All of these animals are living in a zoo
Waiting for someone to bring them their food
These animals are hungry, and I think you know
what I mean when they do their last scream!
The snake slithers
the lion roars
the monkey laughs
the pig snorts
the elephant has...a thought
The rhino is happy now he has his food.

My View

From my view I see the sunrise, it burns so
bright it burns my eyes
In the day I see the sea as the waves splash upon
me
In the morning I watch the trees as they wave in
the air like they're waving to me
I see some birds flying in the air, as they fly in
the blue sky I see something rare
A flying blue bird dancing in the air
As it starts to get dark the waves die down and
the trees slowly stop
Now it is quiet and there is no one to be seen
As I look to the sun setting I just stare until the
sun stops to beam

Celebrations Of The Year

January - Happy new year!

February - Happy Valentines day.

March - Here comes the Spring, hello little chick.

April - Pass me those Easter eggs.

May - Time for good luck.

June - Summers here!

July - Happy Independence day, let's go and play.

August - Where have you been? I have missed you.

September - Back to school, here we go again.

October - Trick or treat? Happy Halloween.

November - Penny for the guy.

December - We wish you a Merry Christmas.

Listen Here

Listen here, for I have so much to say
Even though it is tricky sometimes you must
keep going
Like when I did a long time ago
It was rough and and hard, but I gave it a go
You see life it not easy when are stuck up a
mountain, or cannot answer a question
Just think that some people could be in the same
situation
So listen here, for I have so much to say
Even though it is tricky, sometimes you must
keep going.